Jacob
the Famous Goose of the
2nd Battalion Coldstream Guards

A TRUE STORY

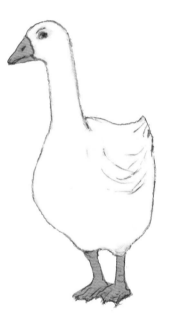

by

Sheila Marlin

A catalogue record of this book is available from the British Library.

ISBN: 978-0-9928459-1-9

Dedication

To the Regimental Adjutants of the Coldstream Guards:

Major A.P. Napier for his permission to write this book.

Colonel Simon Vandeleur who corrected military mistakes
and researched many subjects for me.

Major Cazenove, the Historian who also researched for me.

My writing group for all their help,
Brigid Marlin, Jean Vickery, Shirley Jaworska, Eleanor Callow.

Sisters Olga Marlin, Lis Paice and Brigid Marlin who suggested improvements.

William Callaway who patiently read my book and
helped me to improve and market the book.

June Pearson who gave me many good suggestions.

Nigel Mitchell, my wonderful designer, who has worked endlessly to help me create this book.

Finally, a thank you to the Coldstream Guards who looked after Jacob with such care and
affection between 1838 and 1846 enabling me to write this story.

Other books by Sheila Marlin

A Grandparents Survival Guide to Childcare
co-author with Lis Paice, Bloomsbury Publishers 2013

Flip to the Rescue
Sheila Marlin, self published 2014

Produced in the UK by Shore Books and Design
www.shore-books.co.uk

The *HMS Atholl*

My name is John Kemp. I was a Coldstream Guardsman and I have an extraordinary tale to tell of great heroism from the most unexpected places. It is the story of real friendship and devotion and it all started on April 17th 1838, when I was 18 years old and sailed from Portsmouth to Canada on the troop ship *HMS Atholl.* It was a long, rough journey and I spent a great deal of time leaning over the side of the ship, being seasick. I made friends with James, who had flaming red hair and a great sense of humour. Together we were able to spot dolphins and whales; a wonderful sight! The ship looked splendid with its numerous sails billowing out in the wind. I soon made many other pals. We played cards and competitive games: the Coldstream versus the Grenadier Guards, who were sailing with us. Near the end of the voyage, an officer told us what we might expect in Québec. He warned us that there had been a battle in a nearby town, and I realised that I might have to fight. When he had finished talking, there was a great silence. The fun was over and now we had to face danger. We were told that some French Canadians, calling themselves 'Patriotes', were not happy with English rule in Canada, and were fighting for reforms. Our regiment, with the Grenadiers, had come to keep the peace in this British colony.

When we arrived, we were taken to the Quebec Citadel Headquarters where guards were sent to points around the town. Some of us Coldstreamers were taken from there by horse-drawn carriages to a large farmhouse, set in beautiful countryside. We were to guard this property which supplied food to the soldiers in Québec but it was also suspected of being a secret haunt of rebels. I was born on a farm in Devon so I felt at home. The farmhouse residents were welcoming and we were shown to our rooms after supper. I shared mine with five others. One of them was James! We introduced ourselves and discussed the likelihood of going into battle. The two younger ones, Simon and James, looked upset while the two older ones, Anthony, who was the tallest, and George, with a beard, had already experienced combat so they looked quite calm. The next day we had an official meeting and were given our duties. Our main job was to guard and patrol the perimeters of the farm, keeping a sharp lookout for any trouble.

The first months went by peacefully. When not on duty, my roommates and I took the opportunity to walk and visit the farm animals, especially the horses.

One fine morning I was on duty at a sentry post overlooking the farm buildings. The weather had changed and the trees were dressed in Autumn colours. I was admiring the scene when I noticed, in the distance, movement in the undergrowth. I immediately became attentive.

There was a sudden flash of white, so I got ready with my bayonet. I feared there would be trouble. Would I have to fight, all on my own? I was ready to fire for help from my musket. But, to my relief, it was only a goose emerging from the long grass, loudly squawking and flapping its wings. Behind, a fox was in pursuit, intent to make a meal of it. The goose spotted me and began to run in my direction. I was unable to use my gun as that would unnecessarily signal the alarm to the other guards, a punishable offence, nor could I leave my post. The goose seemed to know I was a friend and came straight towards me. I held my bayonet at the ready.

The fox came close enough to bite off a tail feather, just as the goose lunged between my legs where it felt safe. I lowered the sharp point of my bayonet and killed the fox.

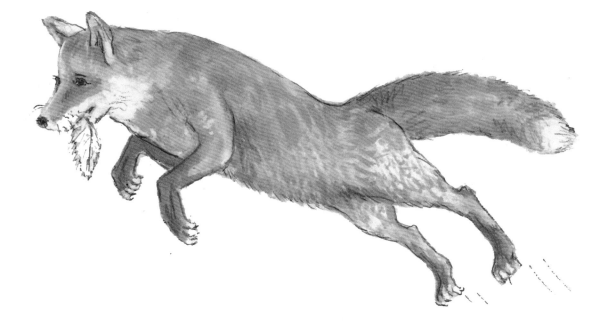

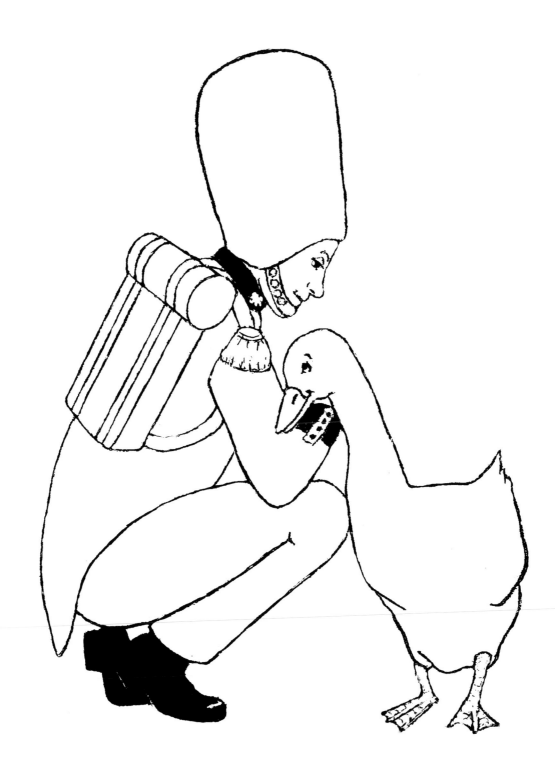

Then I stooped down to pat the exhausted goose that showed its gratitude by nuzzling me with its head and by making curious noises of joy. At the end of my sentry duty, I picked it up and carried it to the farmhouse to check it over and see if it had been hurt. I saw that he was a gander. The other guards watched me carrying this lovely plump goose and asked if it was to be their supper. I could see the greed in their faces at the thought of such a splendid feast. But as I looked down at the bird, I realised that I had already grown fond of this creature which had shown me such trust and affection and even now was content to stay in my arms.

"No," I said firmly, "this is a special goose, not to be eaten."

I pondered what to do and decided I would find an opportunity to hide him in the barn for the night, to keep him safe, just in case.

The next day I rose early to set the gander free. I opened the door cautiously and the bird came forward to greet me. But instead of running off, he followed me, while I did a couple of hours of duty. He did not leave me but just trotted alongside, keeping me company. I was amused and touched by this loyal bird. But I was worried about his safety with all those guards only too happy to put him in the pot. Again, that night I settled him in the barn. And again he followed me the next morning. The remarkable thing was that the gander started marching, even goose-stepping along beside me. Not only had he trust in me but soon this included the other guards as they went on duty. He waddled after each successive sentry and even imitated their military manner. He never seemed to tire and he took his duties as a guard very seriously. I gradually became less worried about the soldiers eating the gander as they grew fond of him. But I still kept a close watch over him and shut him up every night in the barn as a precaution.

After a week, my roommates and I went for a tea break in the farmhouse kitchen where we decided to choose a name for the goose.

"How about Lucky?" proposed James.

Or "Goosey, Goosey?" laughed George through his beard.

"Downey?" suggested Simon, the soft hearted fellow.

"I have thought of a great name. How about Snow White?" said Anthony.

This was greeted with great laughter. "He is a gander," they reminded him.

I thought of names, looking down at the goose next to me. "I think as he always follows us, that we should call him Jacob. That means: *One who follows.*"

"He certainly does that," they all agreed. And so he was named Jacob from then on.

The cook smiled, "Well, we can forget about goose for Christmas dinner. We cannot eat a goose with a name."

'I should think not," retorted the shocked guards.

So Jacob seemed safe for now. After seeing my friends' reaction to the cook, I decided to trust them and ask them to help me to keep Jacob secure.

The gander soon answered to the name of Jacob. He learned all the steps the guards made and he knew when to stand at attention. He could not be tempted to leave his post but walked up and down every day with each sentry that was placed there, looking straight ahead. Jacob was becoming everyone's pet but he favoured me as I had saved his life. He always sought me out and rubbed his neck against my leg or honked at me in a special endearing way. We had become really close.

Jacob sometimes used my time off duty to go with me to meet the other creatures around the farm. He made friends with Shirley, the sheep, and

Cheeky, the chipmunk, who was able to survey the world from the treetops. Cheeky would often turn up in different places to watch us.

We would go for walks in the nearby woods or even go for a swim in the lake if the weather was warm. Jacob loved the water. He was much faster at swimming than me.

Before the weather turned cold, my friends and I decided to build Jacob a miniature sentry box, next to the large one, at the entrance to the farmhouse, for shelter during the day. Jacob seemed proud to have his own sentry box. At strategic points on the farm there were 6 guards on duty at any one time, changing every two hours. At night, I continued to keep Jacob in the barn where it was warmer. It was just as well that he had cover as November came with an abundance of snow. I have never felt so cold. I wore my coat, a winter hat, gloves and moccasins, much warmer than leather boots.

One day, after my duty was completed, we took a stroll and passed the neighbouring farmhouse. Walking kept us both warm. Pierre, the friendly farmer, stopped and told me that he had seen suspicious looking men prowling around near our farm. I thanked him as he rode off by sleigh, laden with food for the citadel. (Most farmers at that time were very poor so Pierre was fortunate to supply the army). I hurried back home to warn everyone to be aware of possible trouble.

I was sad to leave Canada but pleased that I would see my family again. I walked up the hill with Jacob, so that we could have a great view over the countryside. I could spot the chimney of the farmhouse on the right. I said goodbye to the farm, remembering all the happy years I had spent there.

"But I will be glad to get away from the cold winters," I told Jacob, "and you will prefer it too."

The day of departure arrived, 5 October, 1842. The guards boarded the ship 'Calcutta', and we carried Jacob, and his little sentinel box, on board.

On calm days Jacob walked along the deck with me and my friends, who watched over him as well so that he did not come to harm. For a lead, we tied a cord around him. When the boat sailed into bad weather and rough seas, Jacob was not allowed outside in case he was blown overboard. I often joined him in his cabin to calm him down as his stomach was unsettled. We experienced very bad storms for many days. Towards the end of the voyage huge waves came and water flowed over the deck. Jacob and the soldiers felt very sick. But, thankfully, we arrived safely in England.

Jacob and the Regiment went to live at the Coldstream Guards headquarters in the Portman Street Barracks in London. Jacob had his own pond and his small sentinel box in the grounds. He had been adopted in England as the 'Official Coldstream Mascot'. He often saw me and my friends on and off duty but he also made new friends. Jacob liked to march with the sentries around the grounds and outside the barracks' entrance or inside Portman Square Park. He had become very independent.

Jacob's fame spread. Londoners flocked to see him, but he wouldn't allow anyone to disturb him when he was on duty. There were nannies with their charges that waved to Jacob and gave him food to eat. The children loved to visit Jacob and called out to see if they could distract him from his post. But Jacob would never turn his head as he waddled to and fro with the sentries, or stood at 'Attention', until he was off duty. Then he liked strutting around the barracks' walls and making friends, enjoying the offerings and tidbits. He was known to the local residents living on the square who would often give Jacob a treat when he passed by on his way to the park with the regimental band.

He even joined in sentry duty outside the Royal palaces. The Coldstream Guards celebrated special occasions by parading in Horse Guards Parade by St. James's Palace or by changing the guard at Windsor Castle and Buckingham Palace. To these venues we took Jacob as he was our mascot. He always created a stir as he marched along with us. I had been put in charge of his welfare so I kept him close to me. Queen Victoria was resident at Buckingham Palace. Her official birthday was on a Saturday in June, although she had already turned 26 years of age in May, 1845. We were there to take part in the big event of 'Trooping the Colour'. But to our surprise, instead of Queen Victoria, her husband inspected our troops. The Queen had chosen to go incognito with her son, Albert, to mingle in the crowd so that she could enjoy watching her subjects admire her beloved husband. We marched to the music, then, passing the royal dais, we saluted Prince Albert. I could see he was amused by Jacob. Finally we moved away from Horse Guards Parade towards the Buckingham Palace entrance. As we passed the gate, I saw the Queen and Prince Albert and their children waving from the balcony. The Queen and her son had returned earlier and the Prince arrived before us on his horse. Later that day they attended the festive dinner and their grand Costume Ball in the Palace.

Some days later, I received a message from the Queen, asking me to bring Jacob to the Palace, following a request from her children. I was thrilled but also a bit nervous. On the appointed day, after a good wash and polish, we both went to the Palace and I rang the bell. A butler appeared and showed us around the back to the gardens where the Queen greeted us.

"I saw your goose at the 'Trooping the Colour'. He was interested in the goose. My children saw him from the balcony. They are looking forward to meeting this unusual bird. Will they be safe with him?"

I assured her that Jacob was of the gentlest nature. "He loves children and often meets them." Then a nursemaid brought out the children.

Their names and ages were Vicky 4, Albert 3, Alice 2 and baby Alfred, 10 months. When they saw Jacob, they were excited. They approached him, and as he was not on duty, he responded to the children's attentions. Queen Victoria was delighted and called for refreshments to be served outside. I regaled them with the story of Jacob and how he had saved my life. After a delicious spread and delicacies for Jacob, the children were taken back to their nursery, but not before they had given Jacob a hug and shook my hand, saying goodbye most sweetly. Queen Victoria thanked me and said it had been a treat for them. I returned to the barracks and eagerly reported to my friends my amazing experience.

The Duke of Wellington, a great friend of Queen Victoria, used to visit Jacob as he admired duty and dedication in any form. The barracks were situated close to Apsley House where the Duke lived. When he retired in 1846, he had more time for such visits. This was the highest honour as the Duke was extremely famous having led the British army and defeated Napoleon at the battle of Waterloo ending the war with France.

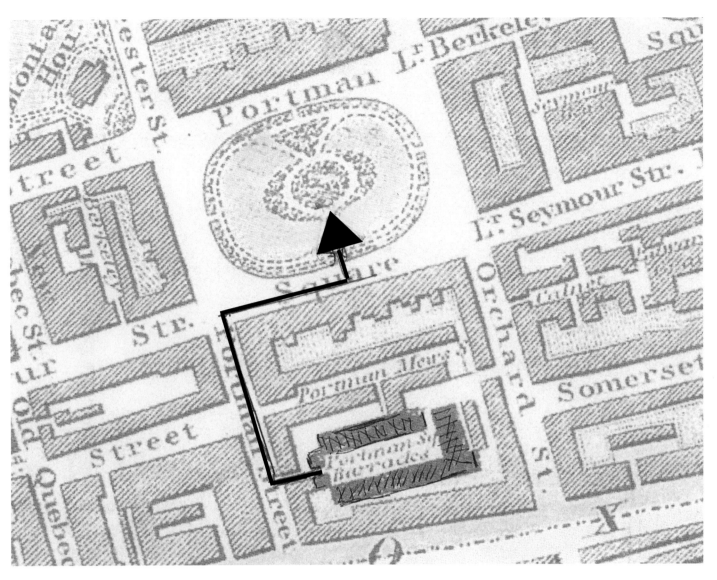

Map of Portman Barracks and the park.

The Coldstream band often played in the grounds or in the square. Jacob took it upon himself to keep the crowd back, especially 'local young boys', by marching with measured pace around the outside of the band. He enjoyed stepping in time to the music. The band had a special March called 'Milanollo' for their regiment which they played regularly. It was their signature tune and Jacob knew it by heart.

The guards sometimes attended parties given for special occasions. Jacob was included as he was the mascot of the 2nd Battalion of the Coldstream Guards. We were proud to show him off.

In the picture is an event held in the area between the two Portman Street Barracks which has been covered over and decorated. (If you look closely, you may be able to find Jacob).

Jacob was fortunate to have lived such a charmed life. But one day tragedy struck. I was on duty and we were walking through the narrow gateway which formed the entrance to the Portman Street Barracks' Headquarters. A horse-led hansom cab, whose owner had not seen the goose, came in at speed. Jacob did not have time to move over to the edge and the horse knocked him down. I watched it all happen as if it was in slow motion but I could not have rescued him. Jacob tried to move his head. I gently lifted him up. I could see he had a broken leg and maybe internal damage. I rushed him to the vet who tried to revive this famous little goose. I watched heartbroken as every effort was being made but it was not possible to save him.

I was with him as he was dying, holding him close in my arms. He just looked at me with that trusting, loving expression and peacefully drifted away. I sobbed over his broken body. My brave, loyal little friend had left me forever. It had been a wonderful, joyful time we had had together. There would never be a friend like that again.

Jacob had died like a true soldier at his post after eight years of sentry duty. London friends and all the guards mourned him. His body was buried with 'All Military Honours' at the Portland Street Barracks. The guards who had been in Canada, including James, Simon, Anthony and George, were there as special guests. The 2nd Battalion Coldstream Guards lined up in a magnificent parade to accord him military honours and to salute him by firing a volley of shots. The band drummed while the guards reversed arms, and then they played their special tune: 'Milanollo'. I was chosen to place the Union Flag on Jacob's little coffin. The Duke of Wellington also paid his respects to this special goose, which had devoted his life to guarding those he loved.

The people mourned him and brought flowers which they placed on Jacob's grave. I often visited my little friend in his final resting place. I missed my constant companion. Much later, when I was married and had children, I happily retired on a farm where I kept geese to guard my farm and family, but especially as pets whose company I enjoy every day.

And so ends my extraordinary tale.

Jacob's grave was in the Portland Barracks' grounds. But this building was demolished later on to build Granville Place in 1865 and the grave was covered over. Today you can see Jacob for yourself on view at the Guard's Museum, Birdcage Walk, London SW1.

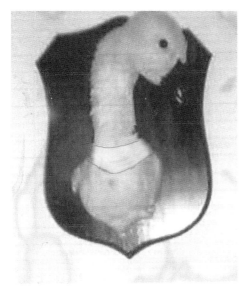

To remember Jacob, the regiment kept and preserved his head and neck, which hadn't been damaged, and put them in a frame on display in the Orderly room, at the Regimental Headquarters' Museum. He still wears his golden collar. The words 'Died on Duty' have been added to the gorget. Later on another goose's body was attached to Jacob's neck and placed in a bigger display cabinet.

Jacob's preserved head.

So Jacob's fame lives on even after all those years. Like their motto, Jacob showed he was 'Second to None', or 'Nulli Secundus'.

The display reads: Alas! Poor Jacob. Enlisted at Québec 1838. Came to England with the 2nd Battalion. He had a good conduct ring.

Jacob in the cabinet.

The End

Background History

Uniform

After the battle of Waterloo, the Coldstream Guards were given the right to wear bearskin caps as a battle honour. They are 18 inches tall and weigh 1.5 pounds. Made from a single Canadian black bear hide, the officers have their caps made out of female furs as they are softer. The male ones are allocated to the soldiers. Their purpose is to make the wearer look taller and more impressive on parade or on the battlefield. Over the years they have become shorter and wider. They are expensive, about £650 each, so they are now limited to guardsmen, bands or other units having a ceremonial role. The British foot soldiers used to wear them into battle and on peacetime manoeuvres until 1902.

The red plumes are made from eagles' feathers for officers, cock feathers for warrant officers and senior NCOs, and all other ranks have horsehair. There are no crowns on the brass buttons of the military corps tunics as they were once part of Cromwell's 'New Model Army'. The groupings of buttons in twos on the tunic is a common way to distinguish the Regiment of Foot Guards. Their buttons are arranged in pairs on their cuffs and tunic, and a Star of the Garter is marked on their brass ware and also worn on the collar. In Winter in Canada, the guards took to wearing moccasins like the Indians wore. With layers of woollen socks as well, they were much warmer than leather boots. Wellingtons like the duke wore, had been fashionable in the eighteen-forties in England but they were initially made in soft calf leather so the rubber ones had not been invented yet! In Jacob's lifetime, the soldiers wore a red coat with tails, navy collar and cuffs, white turn-backs and epaulets, badges, pewter buttons, white trousers and gloves and a bearskin cap with the red plume. The Coldstreamers have changed their clothes over the years. Now they wear dark navy trousers and white cuffs and collar, a longer jacket and a belt. The Changing the Guards at Buckingham Palace shows the regiment in all its discipline, parading in their immaculate uniform.

The name gorget came from the French 'Gorge' meaning throat. It was the armour to protect the neck in battle. It was no longer needed as a piece of armour but was still being worn as a decorative item in those days.

Gorget

The guard

An officer

Battle of Inkerman 1854, still wearing the same uniform.

Left: Private, Coldstream Guards, Winter Dress 1838-40.

Guard by sentry box

Guards in Snowstorm, 1842

History of the Coldstream Guards

Oliver Cromwell raised the 'New Model Army' in 1650. With the civil war over, Cromwell, as Lord Protector, had complete power in England. In the same year he created a new army out of existing regiments and called it the 'New Army'. He then formed the 'Monck's Regiment of Foot' from which the Coldstream Guards are direct descendants and the oldest foot soldiers in continuous service with the British Army. Prince Charles Stuart (the future Charles II), who had landed in Scotland to reclaim his Kingdom, went into battle with Cromwell at Dunbar. Cromwell and his Monck's Regiment were victorious and Charles fled back to France. Cromwell died in 1658 and, as political confusion reigned, there followed unrest in London. Exiled Charles took over the regiment in 1660 to help him win back the throne of England. Led by General Monck (who had now changed his allegiance to the King), the soldiers marched from the small town of Coldstream on the river Tweed in Scotland, from where they got their name, and walked 420 miles for five long weeks to London. They were exhausted and their feet were sore yet they managed to quell the riots and to overcome the Rump Parliament. Monck took it upon himself to bring order in the country. The new Parliament voted Charles back on the throne to become King Charles II. Monck went to greet him at the port as he arrived back in England. Charles was so grateful for his help that he made Monck the Duke of Albemarle and he received the 'Order of the Garter', a great honour which is the reason for the regimental cap star on the uniform. The new parliament passed an act to disband the entire 'New Model Army' which included Monck's 'Regiments of Foot and Horse'. A concession was made that they should be the last to leave. But in 1661 a revolt arose in London two days before the army was to be disbanded, so Charles called for Monck's soldiers to help and they restored peace. The King decided to issue a warrant authorising the establishment of a standing army, the birth of the British Army. Parliament gratefully repealed the order of disbandment of Monck's men. King Charles marched the soldiers to Tower Hill where he renamed them 'The Lord General's Regiment of Foot Soldiers', and they became the 'Household Troops' in the newly established army. A Royal Commission placed them as the second senior Regiment but the troops felt they should have been the first, especially as they were now the oldest regiment in the army. In 1670 they became known as the 'Coldstream Regiment of Foot Guards'. The main purpose of the Foot Guards was to protect the Royal Family in their residences at Buckingham House, St. James's Palace, Windsor Castle and to provide a guard at the Tower of London.

Since then they have fought in every major campaign in Britain's history. Today they are divided into groups: the Regimental Band, the Veterans Association and the Regimental Headquarters, the 1st Battalion and the Number 7 Company that performs ceremonial duties in London and Windsor as part of the Household Division in addition to being fully operational soldiers! They provide a guard for the Queen's birthday parade. Duties also include the State Opening of Parliament, Trooping the Colour and the Changing the Guard. Their motto is 'Nulla Secundus' or 'Second to None'. The Coldstream way is one of 'relaxed efficiency, tempered by discipline of the highest order'. They make a point of being punctual and are always 5 minutes early. they are recognised by the red plumes on the right side of the bearskin caps.

THE "COLDSTREAMERS' (MONCK'S REGIMENT) 1661

The Duke of Wellington

Arthur Wellesley, the first Duke of Wellington, was born in Dublin in 1769. He attended Eton and then joined the army at 18 years of age. In 1805 he met Vice Admiral Horatio Nelson and they discussed the state of colonies and war as equals. Wellesley recalled: 'I don't know when I have ever had a conversation that interested me more!' They never met again as Nelson was killed seven weeks later at Trafalgar.

Wellesley fought from 1808-1814 in the Peninsula War, forcing the French out of Spain and Portugal. In the same year the allied forces of Austria, Russia and Prussia invaded France and caused Napoleon Bonaparte to abdicate from being Emperor, for the sake of peace in Europe. He was exiled to the island of Elba but he escaped after a year and returned to France. He travelled to Paris recruiting soldiers on the way, and once again became Emperor. He moved North with his troops to Belgium. Wellesley was obligated to return to Belgium. He was attending a ball on the 15 June, 1815 in Brussels given by the Duchess of Richmond, when he heard that Napoleon was on the move. Having recently been put in charge of the Anglo-Allied forces, Wellesley commanded his army to travel South. He rode on his special war horse called Copenhagen. He said once, 'The only thing I am afraid of is fear'. The armies met at Waterloo on June 18th. After heavy fighting involving a total of 145,000 men Wellesley defeated Napoleon. Overall 50,000 men died in that battle. After the high cost of his men at Waterloo, Wellesley broke down in tears. He said: 'Believe me, nothing except a battle lost can be half so melancholy as a battle won'.

Copenhagen   Apsley House

Bonaparte was forced to abdicate under the terms of the Treaty of Paris (1815), and was then exiled to the remote island of St. Helena where he died. The Napoleonic Wars had lasted 23 years, with constant warfare in Europe. When Wellesley returned to England, he was hailed as a hero and created the Duke of Wellington. He had fought in many battles, numbering about 60 in total. Wellington was a great leader, especially at defensive tactics which cost his army fewer losses. He received many medals, the most important being the 'Grand Cross of the Most Honourable Knight of the Order of the Garter'. He was made Field Marshall and Commander in Chief of the army. By this time Britain had become the world's dominant power.

Duke of Wellington

The Duke's Portrait

Parliament Building on Fire by J.M.W, Turner

The stone sarcophagus containing the Duke.

The Duke was Prime Minister from 1828 to 1830 and briefly in 1834. He became unpopular when he rejected a reform which the people favoured. Some individuals felt so strongly, they threw rocks at the windows of his house. So he had iron shutters installed to protect his property, earning him the nickname of 'The Iron Duke'. The Duke became the Leader of the House of Lords in 1841. Their meeting place was in temporary accommodation because the ancient Parliament buildings were being rebuilt since 1840, after having been destroyed by fire in 1834. This was caused by two cartloads of wooden tally sticks being burnt in two old cellar furnaces, which were unable to contain the heat. Fire spread from the House of Lords to the rest of the Palace of Westminster, where the Parliament used to be. The fire was the biggest since the Great Fire of London in 1666. Crowds came to watch including J.M.W. Turner who painted several pictures of the event.

The Duke retired from Parliament in 1846. He bought Apsley House, Number 1, Hyde Park but he also had a magnificent mansion in the country, Stratfield Saye, given to him in 1817 by Parliament as a reward for all is triumphs in war. It cost £263,000 (about £8,000,000 today). It was filled with treasures and gifts he received from foreign governments and authorities in England. He died on 18 November, 1852 at the age of 83, after a stroke. He had the most ornate and spectacular state funeral. Over one and a half million people attended the procession through London, which showed the respect and affection the nation had for this heroic man. He was buried in a sarcophagus in St. Paul's Cathedral, next to one for Lord Nelson. After the funeral Lord Alfred Tennyson wrote his poem: 'Ode to the Death of the Duke of Wellington'.

Wellington's horse Copenhagen, named after a battle previously won, was a powerful horse. Wellington said: 'There may have been many faster horses, no doubt many handsomer, but for bottom and endurance I never saw his fellow. His enduring qualities were often attributed to his Arabian blood'. and 'He never refused his corn but had a unique habit of eating while lying down'. Copenhagen spent his retirement years at Stratfield Saye and was buried there next to an ancient tree at the age of 28.

Sir James Macdonnell

Lieutenant Colonel James Macdonnell fought in the Battle of Waterloo against Napoleon's army. He was sent by Wellesley to occupy and defend the Château de Hougoumont with the 2nd Battalion Coldstream Guards. The French had managed to break open the north gate of the farm of Hougoumont with an axe. They then forced the wooden gates open. Macdonnell, with a small group, fought his way through the invading army and tried to close the gates by sheer strength. A soldier called James Graham was able to slot the bar in place. The guards piled up carts, flagstones and debris to keep the gates shut. This allowed the remaining Coldstreamers to fight hand to hand and kill all the French soldiers bar one within the compound. They saved the life of a young drummer boy. It was a near miraculous event. Later Wellington said: 'The success of the battle turned upon the closing of the gates of Hougoumont. The bravest men of the battle were James MacDonnell and James Graham.' As a reward for his bravery, MacDonnell was given £1,000. That was equal to around £30,000 nowadays. He immediately shared this with James Graham.

In May, 1838 Macdonnell was posted to Québec Citadel to be Officer in charge of the British Battalion of Guards. He was sent over by Lord Durham, (newly appointed as Governor-in-Chief of the British North American Colonists) to take charge in Canada. Durham resigned months later as he received no support from Melbourne for his recommendation that Upper and Lower Canada be united. It took ten years for this to finally take place. When the troops were leaving Québec Sir James MacDonnell was also not required to stay any longer so he returned to England, probably on the same boat as Jacob!

Closing the gates

Find the drummer boy

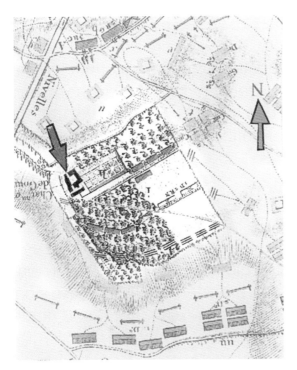

Map of Hougoumont

Sir James Macdonnell

The Canadian Rebellion 1837-1838

After the Seven Years War, the colony of Canada owned by the French, was given to Great Britain. In 1834 the 92 resolutions presented for reform by the French Canadians to the British were ignored. The dissatisfied Patriotes began to get agitated. The number of British troops in Upper Canada (now called Ontario) and Lower Canada (now called Québec), was increased to over ten thousand men. Sentries performed guard duty in Québec citadel where it was peaceful apart from the occasional skirmish. William Mackenzie had made efforts to create peace in Upper Canada. The rebellions prompted the Governor-in-Chief Lord Durham to write the Durham report, which proposed linking the two provinces.

Durham had pardoned the French in exile and was censured by London for this action and so he subsequently resigned. On November 1st, two days after he departed, the exiles who had returned, put in action their planned uprising. Martial Law was proclaimed on the 4th November. There followed several battles, mostly dealt with by the Grenadiers in the Montreal area. Furious riots, charging troops, Canada was in turmoil because of the rebellion against the representatives of young Queen Victoria, after only six months on the throne. The insurgents decided a change in the Government could not be achieved without a fight. They also thought that Britain would back down if faced by an uprising.

On the 23rd November the rebellion began in Lower Canada in the Richelieu valley. The Patriotes, led by Wolfred Nelson, defended Saint-Denis and they defeated the British troops as the latter had run out of ammunition!

The next battle took place on the 25 November, 1837, led by Colonel Wetherall. There were 420 soldiers attacking the camp of Saint-Charles where about 80 insurgents were defending it, an unequal fight. Some Patriotes retreated and their leader, General Thomas Brown, fled at the first shot. Others surrendered so, thinking they had won the battle, the British walked up to surround them and taken unawares, the Patriotes opened fire, killing three soldiers. This trick made the British soldiers furious and they massacred the rebels, leaving many dead.

Saint-Eustache was attacked by 1,500 troops on 14 December, 1837. The cavalry picketed one side of the village, their guns ready, and they ordered the rebels to surrender, but they defied them. So the soldiers bombarded the nearby church and convent. The church caught fire and 66 defenders inside were killed while only one British soldier died! The survivors were taken as prisoners. After, the soldiers burnt the village of Saint-Benoit to the ground. There was widespread looting and burning of the their homes.

The insurgents soon took heart again. Early in 1838, they began raiding loyalists' homes. Cavalry were called out once more. The upheaval came at Beauharnois, and martial law was proclaimed on November 9th. The Grenadiers who came over on the *HMS Atholl* were sent to join this battle. Sir James Macdonnell led them to Nassierville where 3,000 rebels were waiting but dispersed on their approach, many escaping in the woods. Up to 300 surrendered as prisoners. Hundreds were arrested for treason, some were sent to the penal colony in Australia. Seventeen were hung. The British burned everything in sight, South of Montreal.

In Upper Canada, meanwhile, William Lyons Mackenzie was unable to achieve reform by his peaceful efforts in politics so, encouraged by the Patriotes' rebellion in Lower Canada, he rallied men to join him. His plan was to overthrow the government. He raised a force of 800 men. His headquarters were called Montgomery's Tavern. As there were only a few British troops in Toronto, Mackenzie decided to march there on the 5 December, 1837. However, the soldiers prevented them from reaching the city. Two days later 1,000 militia encountered the rebel forces near Montgomery's Tavern and dispersed them. Later, Mackenzie fled to the United States disguised as a woman.

There were frontier raids where mounted guards were on duty all winter long. Major General Sir James Macdonnell was in command of these King's Dragoon Guards and they remained on the frontier. The blizzards and the cold weather made life difficult for them. By 1 May, 1839, the improved conditions concerning riots enabled the authorities to disband all the militia. The 'Act of Union' took place in 1840. However, the Grenadiers stayed until October 1842, to protect their loyal people, but also to keep order while the reforms were being introduced. They probably returned to England on the 'Calcutta' along with Sir James Macdonnell, the Coldstreamers and Jacob.

Queen Victoria

Although this is a true story, I made up and included a visit to the Royal Family in the Palace gardens, as it is quite possible it could have taken place. The goose was on duty for four years parading outside all the palaces.

Queen Victoria was born in 1819 and lived in Kensington House. Her father, Prince Edward, Duke of Kent, died when she was eight months old. She was close to her uncle Leopold with whom she corresponded, also the Duke of Wellington featured largely in her childhood. He had known her at every stage in her life. He took a personal interest in her. When Victoria became Queen, on the 20 June, 1837 he said, 'If she had been my own daughter, I would not have desired to see her perform her part better.'

When her uncle, William IV, died Victoria became Queen. At twenty years of age she was crowned in Westminster Abbey as Queen of the United Kingdom of Great Britain and Ireland. To rule was an enormous task for her and she needed to break away from her domineering mother, the Duchess of Kent and the Duchess's comptroller, Sir John Conroy. The two of them had formed strict rules called the 'Kensington System' for the upbringing of Victoria, so as to render her meek and dependent on them. They hoped to wield power through her. Victoria hated Conroy and she dismissed him as soon as she became Queen. She housed her mother and Conroy, so as not to see them, in a distant property called Ingestre House in Belgravia Square.

She found guidance in the Prime Minister, Viscount Melbourne. He undertook to train Victoria in politics. He tutored her daily and was given a private apartment in Windsor Castle. The Queen was an eager student and quick to learn, gaining in wisdom. She pursued other interests such as art and regularly wrote in her diary. Wellington

Trooping the colour

Changing the Guard

remarked: 'She was doing credit not only to herself and her mother but to every friend she had, by her perfect fulfilment of what was requested of her. She was an intelligent and graceful young woman, capable of acting and thinking for herself'.

She had earlier met Albert of Saxe-Coburg and she planned to marry him when she was older. Now that she was Queen, she asked him if he would wed her. He came over from Germany and they fell deeply in love with each other. They married in St. James Palace when she was twenty years old (1839). In May that year, Melbourne wished to retire and the prospective Prime Minister was Robert Peel, a Tory, who wanted Victoria to dismiss the wives and daughters of the Whig MPs who were in her personal entourage. The Queen refused so Peel declined to form a government - Melbourne agreed to stay on.

The Queen started to produce offspring. Albert was keen to have as many children as possible to achieve his dream to marry them off to royalty all over Europe. His hope was to secure peace and this was achieved while Victoria was alive. Altogether they produced nine children. Victoria was later known as the Grandmother of Europe.

When Prince Albert died on 14 December, 1861, aged 42, Queen Victoria was heartbroken. She built a monument in Frogmore, Windsor for his resting place and for herself to join him later at her death. She wore black for the rest of her life. She reigned for 63 years and 7 months. She died in 1901 at 81 years of age.

On 6 June, 1845, the Coldstream Guards had their turn (once every 3 years with the Grenadiers, Coldstreamers and Scots, now every 5 years to include the Irish and Welsh troops) to display the 'Trooping the Colour' (The ceremony was performed so that the soldiers could recognise their flag as it was carried down the ranks, a necessity in times of battle. The colours of the flags of the battalions were also a symbol of honour). The Queen in those days did not have to take the salute, so she decided to go incognito on her Official Birthday 1845, taking her young son Albert with her. He may have worn a sailor suit for the occasion. (Usually young boys wore dresses until they were 5 years old. Trousers meant buttons to undo!) Albert was also painted the same year wearing a sailor suit. The young prince started the fashion and families took to dressing their children in nautical uniform. The Royal Navy had become the most powerful in the world so it was a way of showing national pride. Victoria had always shown a marked interest in the troops and personally taken the salute. She had wished to join the crowd this time and be amongst her people, maybe to hear how they felt about her beloved husband who was taking the salute. She may also have needed to get back home early to be ready for the evening celebrations.

The costume ball was held on the 6 June, 1845 at Buckingham Palace. Every guest had to dress in the fashion of a century ago when George II was on the throne. Prince Albert came as King George, in a splendid authentic outfit, much admired and Queen Victoria was so proud of him. She looked equally dashing in her costume.

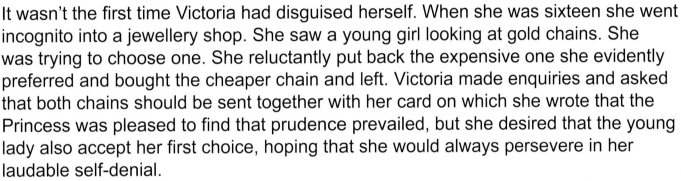

It wasn't the first time Victoria had disguised herself. When she was sixteen she went incognito into a jewellery shop. She saw a young girl looking at gold chains. She was trying to choose one. She reluctantly put back the expensive one she evidently preferred and bought the cheaper chain and left. Victoria made enquiries and asked that both chains should be sent together with her card on which she wrote that the Princess was pleased to find that prudence prevailed, but she desired that the young lady also accept her first choice, hoping that she would always persevere in her laudable self-denial.

In the same year, 1845, Parliament of the Province of Canada passed a statute to officially recognise the Queen's birthday on the 24th of May.

In Ireland the potato famine had begun. The Queen donated £2,000 (nowadays about £140,000) for famine relief.

Victoria was the first Queen to live in Buckingham Palace. It was quite run down and needed renovating. In 1845 she decided to buy Osborne House on the Isle of Wight beside the sea. She paid for it with her own money. She redesigned the layout and had proper plumbing installed, thus avoiding the 1854 'Great Stink' and the outbreak of cholera in London from a central water pump using the Thames contaminated water. The family moved into Osborne House on 19 July, 1845. It was a wonderful playground for the children. A large fort and a Swiss cottage measuring 7½ metres by 15¼ metres were built for them. Queen Victoria had her daughters taught domestic skills in their little house. Prince Albert liked to go swimming nearly every day with his offspring. A bathing machine that went into the water allowed the Queen to bathe without being seen.

In 1876 the Queen was given the title Empress of India. The sun never set on the British Empire which covered a quarter of the world's land mass and population.

Jacob, goose attached to Her Majesty's Regiment of Coldstream Guards. Enlisted at Quebec, Canada, October 1838, and promoted to the post of Superintending the Sentinels. Note the golden gorget-like collar around Jacob's neck. The sentry wears the regiment's uniform: bearskin cap with red plume; red coat with dark blue collar and cuffs, white turnbacks, epaulets, and badges; pewter buttons; white trousers and gloves. Library and Archives Canada, Ottawa, C124921.

This is the only surviving picture of Jacob.

A special piece of music was written by the British composer Martin Ellerby when he was Composer-in-Residence to the Regimental Band Coldstream. He was commissioned to write a work about events in their history which was called: 'Commemorations, The Programme Concert Band'. Amongst the movements, part 3 is a piece for Jacob the Goose called 'Scherzando Militaire' for the 'one time regimental mascot'.

Sources: T.J. Edwards, *Mascots and Pets of the Services* (Aldershot, 1953), 28-33. Gale and Polden Publishers.

Various sites of the Coldstream Guards.